not healed as f***
A journal for us because the
healers need healing too

I'm a therapist and one of my
strong ideologies is that
there is no way a helper can
attempt to restore a healing
soul for others without being
introspective. You hear time
and time again people in the
helping role being burnt out
or unfortunately taken
advantage of by others. It
is my utmost belief that we
can continue to do the work
needed for those around us as
long as we are doing
ourselves justice. We can
only meet people as far as we
can meet ourselves and in the
words of my favorite rapper,

*"We can't heal what we don't
reveal"*

-Jay Z

With a passion to keep the
fire lit in clinicians and
the distaste for people being
taken advantage of, came the
creation of this body of
work.

Perhaps you'll see yourself in these stories. Perhaps one may cause you to get that check-up or deal with past trauma. Maybe, just maybe, it reminds you of why you do the work that you do. I hope this journal can be a source of support for you. You don't have to write in order and you don't have to write every day. Use it as you need. There is a level of vulnerability that is required for people to trust us to help, heal or guide. Let's not take responsibility lightly.

There comes a time for healing, for the healers.

The unique thing about this journal is that you control which stories and which prompt is fitting at the moment. Dates are intentionally missing in case you come back to the same prompt. Below are the topics to help choose where to dive in. There are no rules and no orders. Take what you need. Cheers to getting it out on paper.

Content

"Just because I wear a white coat doesn't mean I'm perfect"

Pharmacist, 2019

Physician, Please Heal Thyself

I believe vulnerability is one of my strongest assets. In the back of my mind once a person learns of a negative experience that someone else had— they can be more prepared and enlightened in their decision-making process. For some reason, titles and credentials can lead people to think that certain professionals should not suffer the same ailments as others. This myth was dispelled for me when I learned that there's an addiction clinic for providers that get addicted to prescription medication.

At one point in time, I experienced a relationship that wasn't the best for me, mentally or spiritually. While there were people in my corner who supported me, there were also questions as to how I could be in a situation so damaging, when I was an expert in helping. One thing for sure is even as a therapist,

"We are not immune to the human experience"

Of course, there's a general belief that you do better as you learn. However, as a facilitator of learning from students, there is a vast amount of space between learning and application.

Should we be held to a standard? Absolutely! Does that mean that those of us in the helping profession will not have low points? I do not think so. The added anxiety to never fail because we have a title in the front or

behind our name shadows our
thoughts dearly.

It also may be unrealistic to
think that we can facilitate
our own healing processes.
Every now and again, we can
benefit from relinquishing
our burdens onto others.
Allowing someone else to hear
our story. So no, physician—
you may not always be able to
heal yourself. Sit in the
space to learn from your
mistakes and even the space
of others. Consider the power
in reaching out to someone
else to filter and aid that
healing process.

Have you ever received
differential treatment
because of your profession?

_____

_____

_____

_____

_____

_____

_____

_____

_____

_____

_____

_____

_____

_____

_____

_____

_____

_____

_____

_____

_____

_____

_____

_____

_____

_____

_____

_____

Is there a level of guilt
knowing you get preferential
treatment?

_____

_____

_____

_____

_____

_____

_____

_____

_____

_____

_____

_____

_____

_____

_____

_____

_____

_____

_____

_____

_____

_____

_____

_____

_____

_____

_____

Write about a time you felt
you could never mess up.

How does the idea of
perfectionism help or hurt?

_____
_____
_____
_____
_____
_____
_____
_____
_____
_____
_____
_____
_____
_____
_____
_____
_____
_____
_____
_____
_____
_____
_____
_____
_____
_____
_____

Tell about a time you were anxious.

_____
_____
_____
_____
_____
_____
_____
_____
_____
_____
_____
_____
_____
_____
_____
_____
_____
_____
_____
_____
_____
_____
_____
_____
_____
_____
_____
_____

What are your barriers to
asking for help?

_____
_____
_____
_____
_____
_____
_____
_____
_____
_____
_____
_____
_____
_____
_____
_____
_____
_____
_____
_____
_____
_____
_____
_____
_____
_____
_____

Tell who you are without
mentioning your profession.

_____
_____
_____
_____
_____
_____
_____
_____
_____
_____
_____
_____
_____
_____
_____
_____
_____
_____
_____
_____
_____
_____
_____
_____
_____
_____

When was the last time you
were vulnerable with someone?

_____

_____

_____

_____

_____

_____

_____

_____

_____

_____

_____

_____

_____

_____

_____

_____

_____

_____

_____

_____

_____

_____

_____

_____

_____

_____

Free write.

Free write.

Childhood Trauma, Is That You?

If you ask most people why they joined a profession that may appear to be low balled, needed in society but very unappreciated and thankless; most likely they'll tell you an experience that was very moving and brought character to their life.

As a clinician who practices from the Psychodynamic Perspective, I am a firm believer that what occurred during our childhood, plays a role in who we are as adults.

For some of us, we may suppress traumatic images. This could be a defense mechanism if something is too heavy of a burden to manage. For others, we may not acknowledge it, because to do that would make it true. Another perspective is if the trauma was normalized. We may mature through life believing other families function in

this way, so what's the
issue.

*"We have all been conditioned
to function in our
dysfunction"*

This can translate in a
variety of ways as you
navigate through your life's
work. You may be a teacher
wishing to adopt every
student that comes into class
appearing to be uncared for
and shown affection. You may
cry daily on your way home
from work, repeatedly stating
you are weeping for another
when it's really your
childhood self. You may treat
a parent with indifference
when they remind you of your
own; you justify it saying
that the child also known as
you— deserves better.

Yet, the gag is in the
effects of trauma it can
display itself in a variety
of ways. It seems so innocent
and under the radar until we
are triggered, that it can go

untreated for quite some
time.

Why did you decide to go into
the helping profession?

_____
_____
_____
_____
_____
_____
_____
_____
_____
_____
_____
_____
_____
_____
_____
_____
_____
_____
_____
_____
_____
_____
_____
_____
_____
_____
_____

Have you noticed anything parallel to your childhood occurring?

_____
_____
_____
_____
_____
_____
_____
_____
_____
_____
_____
_____
_____
_____
_____
_____
_____
_____
_____
_____
_____
_____
_____
_____

Has anything prompted you to
want to seek professional
help to process through
things?

_____
_____
_____
_____
_____
_____
_____
_____
_____
_____
_____
_____
_____
_____
_____
_____
_____
_____
_____
_____
_____
_____
_____

Tell about a memory from
childhood that brings a smile
to your face.

_____
_____
_____
_____
_____
_____
_____
_____
_____
_____
_____
_____
_____
_____
_____
_____
_____
_____
_____
_____
_____
_____
_____
_____
_____
_____

Do you currently work with
children in your profession?
Why or why not?

_____
_____
_____
_____
_____
_____
_____
_____
_____
_____
_____
_____
_____
_____
_____
_____
_____
_____
_____
_____
_____
_____
_____
_____
_____
_____
_____

Have situations from childhood impacted your desire or ability to have children?

_____

_____

_____

_____

_____

_____

_____

_____

_____

_____

_____

_____

_____

_____

_____

_____

_____

_____

_____

_____

_____

_____

_____

How are you similar or
different from your parents?

_____
_____
_____
_____
_____
_____
_____
_____
_____
_____
_____
_____
_____
_____
_____
_____
_____
_____
_____
_____
_____
_____
_____
_____
_____
_____

Tell about a family tradition
you want to create.

_____

_____
_____
_____
_____
_____
_____
_____
_____
_____
_____
_____
_____
_____
_____
_____
_____
_____
_____
_____
_____
_____
_____
_____
_____

Free write.

_____
_____
_____
_____
_____
_____
_____
_____
_____
_____
_____
_____
_____
_____
_____
_____
_____
_____
_____
_____
_____
_____
_____
_____
_____
_____
_____
_____
_____

Free write.

I still show up for my inner
child by having fun in this
way.

_____
_____
_____
_____
_____
_____
_____
_____
_____
_____
_____
_____
_____
_____
_____
_____
_____
_____
_____
_____
_____
_____
_____
_____
_____
_____

I See Me On The Couch

There's a therapist who
shared her story on how she
sees herself on the couch.
She described the connection
between herself and clients
that are impacted by
addiction for example, due to
her own family history.

Occasionally, I meet with a
client and they tell me my
own story. I sit there with
my therapist face and give
the appropriate responses,
all the while thinking, shit—
that's me. The relation is
like seeing myself in the
same image, but in someone
else's mirror. I sat down
with a colleague and asked
what it means to see herself
on the couch. Here is her
story:

Often times on my couch, I
see a broken woman who
struggled with abandonment
issues that I had to work
through in therapy. This
could also look like a

damaging great relationships
out of fear, leaving before
someone left me, being afraid
to love fully and being
fearful of being accepted
with trust issues.

I also have a soft spot for
family members of clients who
are impacted by addiction,
being that I experienced this
myself with my dad.
Codependency hits home and to
be honest that also played a
role in how I felt people
viewed me.

Lastly, being newly married—
couples work has started to
weigh on me. If infidelity is
an issue or one not being
good enough for a partner, I
too am triggered.

It wasn't as if she treated
those clients differently,
more so that she could
empathize and had a true
level of understanding. She
also made mention that when
couples come into treatment
with her, being that she is

newly married, there is also a level of empathy activated.

I've met some people in the helping profession that describes in great detail how their education helped to prepare them for the human exchange that takes place when working with other individuals. In social work, it's defined by countertransference.

Countertransference refers to the clinicians' reaction to the client. Transference, which may come up as well, is the client's reaction to the clinician (Goldstein, 1995).

This could look like a client reminding you of someone in your life. Again, a very normal experience. It's important to emphasize the appropriateness of our actions that follow. Most professions have a code of ethics around the boundaries of professional relationships. When there is a power differential, it is imperative that we stick to that.

There is a reason why most of us are required to participate in an internship, externship or practicum. This is the time to learn not just about our field, but also to build that relationship with your supervisor. If some things are coming up for you as you sit with a client, then we would articulate ourselves during supervision. It's also nice to keep a group of peers that can keep you accountable.

Even if you aren't ready to get on the couch, make sure you have a safe place to release.

Ever had a client or patient that reminded you of someone you know?

_____

_____

_____

_____

_____

_____

_____

_____

_____

_____

_____

_____

_____

_____

_____

_____

_____

_____

_____

_____

_____

_____

_____

_____

_____

In school or in training— was there preparation for managing your feelings while working with others?

_____
_____
_____
_____
_____
_____
_____
_____
_____
_____
_____
_____
_____
_____
_____
_____
_____
_____
_____
_____
_____
_____
_____
_____
_____
_____
_____

Describe your safe place.

_____
_____
_____
_____
_____
_____
_____
_____
_____
_____
_____
_____
_____
_____
_____
_____
_____
_____
_____
_____
_____
_____
_____
_____
_____
_____
_____

Who supports you in decision making?

_____

_____

_____

_____

_____

_____

_____

_____

_____

_____

_____

_____

_____

_____

_____

_____

_____

_____

_____

_____

_____

_____

_____

_____

_____

_____

_____

_____

Tell about your first time in therapy.

_____

_____
_____
_____
_____
_____
_____
_____
_____
_____
_____
_____
_____
_____
_____
_____
_____
_____
_____
_____
_____
_____
_____
_____
_____
_____
_____
_____
_____
_____

Do your friends and family
support attending to your
mental health?

_____
_____
_____
_____
_____
_____
_____
_____
_____
_____
_____
_____
_____
_____
_____
_____
_____
_____
_____
_____
_____
_____
_____
_____
_____

Describe your ideal therapy
session.

_____
_____
_____
_____
_____
_____
_____
_____
_____
_____
_____
_____
_____
_____
_____
_____
_____
_____
_____
_____
_____
_____
_____
_____
_____
_____
_____
_____

Tell about something you aren't ready to address in therapy yet.

_____

_____

_____

_____

_____

_____

_____

_____

_____

_____

_____

_____

_____

_____

_____

_____

_____

_____

_____

_____

_____

_____

_____

_____

_____

_____

_____

Free write.

Free write.

Why You Never Ready?

Howard University blessed me when they encouraged that we seek therapy on our own prior to practicing. I gave that therapist hell. She was a doctoral student from what I recall and she had to record some of our sessions. This was the first time I could put a name to my sweaty palms, racing thoughts, and prior panic attacks— anxiety. Although I didn't take the sessions serious at the time, that unbeknownst to be started my own journey of healing.

In Therapy and Practice of Counseling and Psychotherapy, they eloquently discuss the counselor as a therapeutic person.

"If we are willing to look at our lives and make the changes we want, we can model that process by the way we reveal ourselves and respond to our clients."

Corey also identifies lessons that we can learn while involved in our own therapeutic process. These include empathy, personal relationships, patience, tolerance, dealing with transference and countertransference (Corey, 2013).

I continued my journey with therapy on and off. Sometimes I can recall a distinctive period in my life where I lived on the edge and was too shameful to see anyone. Often I encourage my friends, interns and even family to "get on the couch."

Does your profession require professional development courses?

_____
_____
_____
_____
_____
_____
_____
_____
_____
_____
_____
_____
_____
_____
_____
_____
_____
_____
_____
_____
_____
_____
_____
_____
_____
_____

Do they encourage mental
health days?

_____

_____

_____

_____

_____

_____

_____

_____

_____

_____

_____

_____

_____

_____

_____

_____

_____

_____

_____

_____

_____

_____

_____

_____

In your current role, is
Employee Assistant Services
or the like cover mental
health treatment?

_____

_____

_____

_____

_____

_____

_____

_____

_____

_____

_____

_____

_____

_____

_____

_____

_____

_____

_____

_____

_____

_____

_____

_____

Tell about your definition of shame.

_____
_____
_____
_____
_____
_____
_____
_____
_____
_____
_____
_____
_____
_____
_____
_____
_____
_____
_____
_____
_____
_____
_____
_____
_____

What is something you've
never told anyone?

_____

_____

_____

_____

_____

_____

_____

_____

_____

_____

_____

_____

_____

_____

_____

_____

_____

_____

_____

_____

_____

_____

_____

_____

_____

Tell about the last situation
that humbled you.

_____
_____
_____
_____
_____
_____
_____
_____
_____
_____
_____
_____
_____
_____
_____
_____
_____
_____
_____
_____
_____
_____
_____
_____
_____
_____
_____
_____

What does readiness mean?

_____

_____

_____

_____

_____

_____

_____

_____

_____

_____

_____

_____

_____

_____

_____

_____

_____

_____

_____

_____

_____

_____

_____

_____

_____

_____

Name three things you want to let go off.

_____
_____
_____
_____
_____
_____
_____
_____
_____
_____
_____
_____
_____
_____
_____
_____
_____
_____
_____
_____
_____
_____
_____
_____
_____
_____
_____

Free write.

Free write.

Free write.

Show Me YOU

Growing up, we learn from our surroundings, how we are supposed to be. The weirdest and cutest thing happening to remind me of that currently, is my 17-month old daughter putting my bras around her neck.

Components of Learning theory help to explain what is occurring with my daughter.

Modeling is the learning of behavior by observing the behavior of another individual engaged in that behavior (Zastrow, C.H., Kirst-Ashman, K.K., 2016). As we get older, the hope is a replacement of who other people think we should be to coming to terms with who we truly are.

It may be a struggle if your family lives vicariously through you. This can also be difficult if who you once thought you were has been

tainted by a betrayal,
mistrust or traumatic event.

One of my neos told me a
story about sending out
headshots in natural hair and
receiving little responses,
versus the huge response once
she straightened her hair and
put herself out there.
This would be explained by
operant conditioning. This is
a type of learning in which
behaviors are influenced
primarily by the consequences
that follow them, (Zastrow,
C.H., Kirst-Ashman, K.K.,
2016). Society may advance
its own image onto you, but I
encourage you to be
authentically who you are.
Take yourself out on some
solo dates so you have an
idea of what you prefer. Be
kind to yourself because you
will progress into a
butterfly.

The best story you can
narrate is your own.

Who is in your support
system?

_____
_____
_____
_____
_____
_____
_____
_____
_____
_____
_____
_____
_____
_____
_____
_____
_____
_____
_____
_____
_____
_____
_____
_____
_____
_____
_____
_____

The last time I made myself
proud was when I

_____

_____

_____

_____

_____

_____

_____

_____

_____

_____

_____

_____

_____

_____

_____

_____

_____

_____

_____

_____

_____

_____

_____

_____

_____

_____

_____

_____

Describe yourself.

_____
_____
_____
_____
_____
_____
_____
_____
_____
_____
_____
_____
_____
_____
_____
_____
_____
_____
_____
_____
_____
_____
_____
_____
_____
_____
_____
_____
_____

Being genuine to yourself
looks like this.

_____

_____

_____

_____

_____

_____

_____

_____

_____

_____

_____

_____

_____

_____

_____

_____

_____

_____

_____

_____

_____

_____

_____

_____

_____

Sometimes I struggle to put
my needs first because

_____

_____

_____

_____

_____

_____

_____

_____

_____

_____

_____

_____

_____

_____

_____

_____

_____

_____

_____

_____

_____

_____

_____

_____

_____

_____

_____

I know I'm good enough
because

_____

_____

_____

_____

_____

_____

_____

_____

_____

_____

_____

_____

_____

_____

_____

_____

_____

_____

_____

_____

_____

_____

_____

_____

_____

I used to journal but stopped
because

_____

_____

_____

_____

_____

_____

_____

_____

_____

_____

_____

_____

_____

_____

_____

_____

_____

_____

_____

_____

_____

_____

_____

_____

_____

_____

_____

Comparing myself to others on
social media has resulted in

_____

_____

_____

_____

_____

_____

_____

_____

_____

_____

_____

_____

_____

_____

_____

_____

_____

_____

_____

_____

_____

_____

_____

_____

_____

_____

I like me because I'm....

_____
_____
_____
_____
_____
_____
_____
_____
_____
_____
_____
_____
_____
_____
_____
_____
_____
_____
_____
_____
_____
_____
_____
_____
_____
_____
_____
_____
_____

Free write.

Free write.

Vices in A Crisis

True life: I'm an emotional spender. There were years of me not having a clue about money, credit or anything related to finances. Fast forward to enlightenment of monetary value. In time I unlearned my bad management skills.

Sometimes when you are working with people on a daily basis, you may begin to feel overwhelmed. You could feel like you need to indulge heavily in one motion or may do some things that could cause harm later although in the moment it feels good.

"All things in moderation"

Some ways I cope after a long
day include

_____
_____
_____
_____
_____
_____
_____
_____
_____
_____
_____
_____
_____
_____
_____
_____
_____
_____
_____
_____
_____
_____
_____
_____
_____
_____
_____
_____

One thing that I struggle to
control is

_____
_____
_____
_____
_____
_____
_____
_____
_____
_____
_____
_____
_____
_____
_____
_____
_____
_____
_____
_____
_____
_____
_____
_____
_____
_____

I am ashamed to admit

_____
_____
_____
_____
_____
_____
_____
_____
_____
_____
_____
_____
_____
_____
_____
_____
_____
_____
_____
_____
_____
_____
_____
_____
_____
_____
_____
_____
_____

Free write.

I'm Triggered, Help!

Somehow we made the decision to lend our hands out. People may have failed to mention how we help ourselves as we help others or we create more confusion for ourselves. I wonder how often does something come up in your work that you didn't possess the energy to face yourself? I had a therapist once that I supervised and on her caseload were a ton of cases pertaining to grief and loss. In her notes though, I saw no mention of grief. When I asked she said it never came up. Later it was revealed she had her own grief in her life that she hadn't yet processed.

We can only meet people are far as we can meet ourselves.

This means there will be things presented that we may struggle with due to internal conflicts. That doesn't mean you would have breakdowns in

the moment, but it may sit
with you at home.

The same process we may use
when clients we have to use
with ourselves. Take note of
things other people say and
don't allow that to bother
you. Know when you need to
take a break from the work. I
can't address my triggers, if
I have no idea where they're
coming from.

Do you cry daily after work?

_____
_____
_____
_____
_____
_____
_____
_____
_____
_____
_____
_____
_____
_____
_____
_____
_____
_____
_____
_____
_____
_____
_____
_____
_____
_____
_____
_____

Have you considered adopting or paying for a client or student?

_____
_____
_____
_____
_____
_____
_____
_____
_____
_____
_____
_____
_____
_____
_____
_____
_____
_____
_____
_____
_____
_____
_____
_____
_____
_____
_____

Are you losing sleep thinking about your patients or clients?

_____
_____
_____
_____
_____
_____
_____
_____
_____
_____
_____
_____
_____
_____
_____
_____
_____
_____
_____
_____
_____
_____
_____
_____

Tell about your baseline
behaviors. You eating
regular, sleeping okay, have
enough energy to function?

_____
_____
_____
_____
_____
_____
_____
_____
_____
_____
_____
_____
_____
_____
_____
_____
_____
_____
_____
_____
_____
_____
_____
_____
_____
_____

Is there a colleague or peers
in your support system that
can understand your day to
day?

_____

_____

_____

_____

_____

_____

_____

_____

_____

_____

_____

_____

_____

_____

_____

_____

_____

_____

_____

_____

_____

_____

_____

_____

_____

_____

Tell about some things you
may need to talk to your boss
or supervisor about.

_____
_____
_____
_____
_____
_____
_____
_____
_____
_____
_____
_____
_____
_____
_____
_____
_____
_____
_____
_____
_____
_____
_____
_____
_____

My triggers are

_____
_____
_____
_____
_____
_____
_____
_____
_____
_____
_____
_____
_____
_____
_____
_____
_____
_____
_____
_____
_____
_____
_____
_____
_____
_____
_____
_____
_____

My ideal client will

_____
_____
_____
_____
_____
_____
_____
_____
_____
_____
_____
_____
_____
_____
_____
_____
_____
_____
_____
_____
_____
_____
_____
_____
_____
_____
_____
_____

My ideal client is not

_____

_____

_____

_____

_____

_____

_____

_____

_____

_____

_____

_____

_____

_____

_____

_____

_____

_____

_____

_____

_____

_____

_____

_____

_____

Free write.

_____
_____
_____
_____
_____
_____
_____
_____
_____
_____
_____
_____
_____
_____
_____
_____
_____
_____
_____
_____
_____
_____
_____
_____
_____
_____
_____
_____

Free write.

Showing Up for Myself-
Imposter Syndrome

One of my good friends is a
nurse practitioner. She is
and has always been one of
the smartest people I know.
Listening to her perspective
on how she got to where she
is today, I was intrigued.
Quite often we may feel like
we are only in a space to
fill a quota, albeit race or
gender based.

Age discrimination can also
show up and comments about
how young we are to fill a
role or micro-aggressions
related to other demographics
may spark the idea that we do
not belong where we are
working.

I encourage you to show up
though. Even if someone
helped you get into a
position, it's because of who
you are that they are keeping
you on. You owe it to you to
yourself that you are not an
imposter.

You belong. You are not a
fraud. You are competent.

I shrink at work because

_____
_____
_____
_____
_____
_____
_____
_____
_____
_____
_____
_____
_____
_____
_____
_____
_____
_____
_____
_____
_____
_____
_____
_____
_____

Sometimes I don't believe I
deserve this role because

_____
_____
_____
_____
_____
_____
_____
_____
_____
_____
_____
_____
_____
_____
_____
_____
_____
_____
_____
_____
_____
_____
_____
_____
_____
_____
_____
_____

My areas of improvement are

_____
_____
_____
_____
_____
_____
_____
_____
_____
_____
_____
_____
_____
_____
_____
_____
_____
_____
_____
_____
_____
_____
_____
_____
_____
_____
_____

I am really good at

_____
_____
_____
_____
_____
_____
_____
_____
_____
_____
_____
_____
_____
_____
_____
_____
_____
_____
_____
_____
_____
_____
_____
_____
_____
_____
_____

My education and experience
prepared me in this way

_____

_____

_____

_____

_____

_____

_____

_____

_____

_____

_____

_____

_____

_____

_____

_____

_____

_____

_____

_____

_____

_____

_____

_____

_____

I celebrate my wins by

_____
_____
_____
_____
_____
_____
_____
_____
_____
_____
_____
_____
_____
_____
_____
_____
_____
_____
_____
_____
_____
_____
_____
_____
_____
_____
_____
_____

I do deserve this role
because

_____
_____
_____
_____
_____
_____
_____
_____
_____
_____
_____
_____
_____
_____
_____
_____
_____
_____
_____
_____
_____
_____
_____
_____
_____
_____
_____
_____
_____

My work matters because

_____

_____

_____

_____

_____

_____

_____

_____

_____

_____

_____

_____

_____

_____

_____

_____

_____

_____

_____

_____

_____

_____

_____

_____

_____

_____

Free write.

_____
_____
_____
_____
_____
_____
_____
_____
_____
_____
_____
_____
_____
_____
_____
_____
_____
_____
_____
_____
_____
_____
_____
_____
_____
_____

Free write.

_____
_____
_____
_____
_____
_____
_____
_____
_____
_____
_____
_____
_____
_____
_____
_____
_____
_____
_____
_____
_____
_____
_____
_____
_____
_____
_____
_____
_____

Don't go ghost

Ghosting is a funny name for a very serious topic. When I initially heard people using the term, I chuckled. Then, as a clinician working with other clinicians and I saw it in action, my concern grew.

So set aside initial assumptions that this is related to dating or friendships. While I don't think ghosting is fitting in those spaces either that's for another day and time.

From the professional standpoint, if you have an interview, appointment or engagement scheduled— you should be there. If you are going to be late, you should call or email or text seeing as we have a million ways to get in contact with people. At the last agency I worked at, in the supervisory role we would have interviews scheduled and the candidate would just not show. I was so

taken aback and thought,
didn't they apply for the
position?

The majority of people that I
know whether they work on a
fee for service schedule or
not— would not like it if
people consistently didn't
show up, so as a
professional, nah as an
adult, why not extend that
same courtesy.

As a person living with
anxiety, I can assume that
plays a huge role. Not
wanting to say you don't
actually want that position
or can't afford to keep the
appointment could be
barriers. But what standard
are we setting if we struggle
with telling someone no thank
you. I used to scoff at
missed appointment and no
call fees until they became
applicable to me.

Lastly, when you ghost or
don't cancel in a fitting
amount of time, you take away

from another person sliding
into that slot.

Pick up the phone and say you
can't make it. Don't go
ghost.

Have you been stood up by someone? What did it feel like?

_____
_____
_____
_____
_____
_____
_____
_____
_____
_____
_____
_____
_____
_____
_____
_____
_____
_____
_____
_____
_____
_____
_____
_____
_____
_____

What, if any, is your no-show or cancellation policy?

_____
_____
_____
_____
_____
_____
_____
_____
_____
_____
_____
_____
_____
_____
_____
_____
_____
_____
_____
_____
_____
_____
_____
_____
_____
_____
_____
_____

How do you value your time?

_____
_____
_____
_____
_____
_____
_____
_____
_____
_____
_____
_____
_____
_____
_____
_____
_____
_____
_____
_____
_____
_____
_____
_____
_____
_____
_____

Are you consistently late
personally or professionally?

_____
_____
_____
_____
_____
_____
_____
_____
_____
_____
_____
_____
_____
_____
_____
_____
_____
_____
_____
_____
_____
_____
_____
_____
_____
_____

Tell about a time you ghosted someone, in the personal or professional sense.

_____
_____
_____
_____
_____
_____
_____
_____
_____
_____
_____
_____
_____
_____
_____
_____
_____
_____
_____
_____
_____
_____
_____
_____
_____
_____
_____

Who helps to keep you
accountable?

_____

_____

_____

_____

_____

_____

_____

_____

_____

_____

_____

_____

_____

_____

_____

_____

_____

_____

_____

_____

_____

_____

_____

_____

Tell about your last
interview for something.

_____

_____

_____

_____

_____

_____

_____

_____

_____

_____

_____

_____

_____

_____

_____

_____

_____

_____

_____

_____

_____

_____

_____

_____

Free write.

Free write.

_____
_____
_____
_____
_____
_____
_____
_____
_____
_____
_____
_____
_____
_____
_____
_____
_____
_____
_____
_____
_____
_____
_____
_____
_____
_____
_____

Free write.

The Power of Being More Than a Student

When I was an intern in the field, I learned some of my toughest lessons. There was a situation I was in that called for me to set my own boundary. I was terrified. A worker at my internship was making inappropriate comments. Of course I went to my supervisor for her to reprimand him and her response had me floored. She told me I needed to talk with him myself. Not only was I young in the field but honestly I wasn't confident in my own capabilities resolve the issue peacefully. That was a lesson in standing up for myself that I will never forget.

I was fortunate at one point to have a paid internship (that I saved no money from). As a student and even as someone who is not all the way equipped to practice independently, this is your

time to mess up and learn
from your mistakes. This is
the opportunity to gain
understanding from
experience. Ask a ton of
questions and show up to the
internship prepared. Study
the company before you go in.
Get familiar with company
culture. Even if it's not the
specialty you want, never
take for granted
opportunities to grasp a
variety of concepts.

Tell me about a tough lesson
learned while interning.

_____
_____
_____
_____
_____
_____
_____
_____
_____
_____
_____
_____
_____
_____
_____
_____
_____
_____
_____
_____
_____
_____
_____
_____
_____
_____

Did you continue professional
or personal relationships
after you finished?

_____
_____
_____
_____
_____
_____
_____
_____
_____
_____
_____
_____
_____
_____
_____
_____
_____
_____
_____
_____
_____
_____
_____
_____
_____
_____
_____

Would your supervisor write a
glowing recommendation, why
or why not?

_____
_____
_____
_____
_____
_____
_____
_____
_____
_____
_____
_____
_____
_____
_____
_____
_____
_____
_____
_____
_____
_____
_____
_____
_____
_____
_____
_____

How did you contribute to
your placement?

_____
_____
_____
_____
_____
_____
_____
_____
_____
_____
_____
_____
_____
_____
_____
_____
_____
_____
_____
_____
_____
_____
_____
_____
_____
_____
_____

I wanted to learn more about

_____
_____
_____
_____
_____
_____
_____
_____
_____
_____
_____
_____
_____
_____
_____
_____
_____
_____
_____
_____
_____
_____
_____
_____
_____
_____
_____
_____

I'm struggling with
_____ but not sure how
to ask for help.

_____
_____
_____
_____
_____
_____
_____
_____
_____
_____
_____
_____
_____
_____
_____
_____
_____
_____
_____
_____
_____
_____
_____
_____
_____
_____
_____

I admire my supervisor
because

_____
_____
_____
_____
_____
_____
_____
_____
_____
_____
_____
_____
_____
_____
_____
_____
_____
_____
_____
_____
_____
_____
_____
_____
_____
_____
_____
_____
_____

Free write.

_____

_____

_____

_____

_____

_____

_____

_____

_____

_____

_____

_____

_____

_____

_____

_____

_____

_____

_____

_____

_____

_____

_____

_____

_____

_____

_____

Free write.

_____
_____
_____
_____
_____
_____
_____
_____
_____
_____
_____
_____
_____
_____
_____
_____
_____
_____
_____
_____
_____
_____
_____
_____
_____
_____
_____

When The Life Vest Deflates

They tell us about burnout but I'm not sure if we have accurate plan on how to prevent it. This story is a friend of a friend from high school who has been a teacher in New York City for the last seven years.

"I just want to teach"

I asked her off the bat about the support in terms of professional development she feels she receives. I can only imagine working with children is a tough job. She discussed having a lack of support and having to develop a lot of her curriculum.

"We were thrown to the wolves"

She mentioned being in a position that serves as a representative for other teachers. She received

223

constant backlash whenever she approached administration with innovation and strategy. When working in a bureaucratic system, there is a deliberate plan that takes place. Many times I question how can I avoid my wants without you knowing.

Working with people on a day to day basis can make you feel like you are in the business of emotions and they never turn off. Pair that with working within a system that you cannot control with limited support, it can feel like no matter how smart you work—you continue to sink.

I can ask these people for
support

_____

_____

_____

_____

_____

_____

_____

_____

_____

_____

_____

_____

_____

_____

_____

_____

_____

_____

_____

_____

_____

_____

_____

_____

My threshold for pain is
(physical and emotional)

_____
_____
_____
_____
_____
_____
_____
_____
_____
_____
_____
_____
_____
_____
_____
_____
_____
_____
_____
_____
_____
_____
_____
_____
_____
_____
_____

I shy away from asking for
support because

_____
_____
_____
_____
_____
_____
_____
_____
_____
_____
_____
_____
_____
_____
_____
_____
_____
_____
_____
_____
_____
_____
_____
_____
_____
_____

Tell about a time someone you
love made you feel unlovable.

_____
_____
_____
_____
_____
_____
_____
_____
_____
_____
_____
_____
_____
_____
_____
_____
_____
_____
_____
_____
_____
_____
_____
_____
_____

These are signs that I need
to rest

_____
_____
_____
_____
_____
_____
_____
_____
_____
_____
_____
_____
_____
_____
_____
_____
_____
_____
_____
_____
_____
_____
_____
_____
_____
_____
_____
_____

Rest is

_____
_____
_____
_____
_____
_____
_____
_____
_____
_____
_____
_____
_____
_____
_____
_____
_____
_____
_____
_____
_____
_____
_____
_____
_____
_____

The last vacation I took was

_____
_____
_____
_____
_____
_____
_____
_____
_____
_____
_____
_____
_____
_____
_____
_____
_____
_____
_____
_____
_____
_____
_____
_____
_____
_____
_____
_____

Free write.

Free write.

Clearing The Emotional Space

Often times clients, students
and even a friend try to slip
in every once and awhile to
leave their emotional
baggage...I mean luggage with
me. Now a part of my role as
a clinician is to help sort
through the mess, however
what happens when I am left
with all the feels and
emotions. If you've taken any
sort of personality test, or
felt this call to altruism,
you are probably the strong
friend in your group of
friends.

Anyone have family that turn
to you or need your attention
as soon as you get home? Just
me. No worries.

The other side to this though
is us setting up boundaries.
My therapist told me in a
jarring way that I had poor
boundaries and I wanted to
let her have it! I refrained,
ONE out decorum but *TWO*

because she was dead ass
right.

Seeing as you probably feel
your purpose is to heal
others, you may have or have
not been labeled the person
that saves. I don't want you
to get lost in other people's
stuff. Sometimes we have to
empty out our closet, office,
headspace of other people's
dead weight so we can have
room for our own.

Decompression is probably one
of my top five favorite
activities. This is defined
as releasing from pressure
and relaxing, (Merrian-
Webster).
Initially leaving school,
they rally around self-care
but you end of working for
many systems that do not
support it in a viable way.
Productivity can be a huge
requirement of your work or
you may feel guilty for using
your paid time off.

It may be difficult to take time off or the expectation may be set that you want to cut off needed routine times like eating or sleeping to achieve more. That sets the current generation apart is that we often take vacation and mental health days and sick days. I want to speak directly to the person who always feel they need a break from life. Or the person who doesn't believe in breaks.

Working with people on a daily basis takes skills. It requires boundaries and a certain amount of faith in the profession. In the attempt to combat a burn out culture, I'm often speaking with others about the power of decompression. This is different for everyone but it could be driving home in silence, not answering the phone after work, or even going for a walk when you get home. This is the best routine for you to relax after work.

If you spend the majority of your workday putting out fires so to speak, you may need some time to reset. This will require you to establish some boundaries not just with clients but also with yourself.

How do you decompress?

_____
_____
_____
_____
_____
_____
_____
_____
_____
_____
_____
_____
_____
_____
_____
_____
_____
_____
_____
_____
_____
_____
_____
_____
_____
_____
_____
_____

What do you do with the
stories you may collect from
clients or patients?

_____
_____
_____
_____
_____
_____
_____
_____
_____
_____
_____
_____
_____
_____
_____
_____
_____
_____
_____
_____
_____
_____
_____
_____
_____
_____

Who listens to your story?

_____
_____
_____
_____
_____
_____
_____
_____
_____
_____
_____
_____
_____
_____
_____
_____
_____
_____
_____
_____
_____
_____
_____
_____
_____
_____

Tell about your emotional baggage.

_____
_____
_____
_____
_____
_____
_____
_____
_____
_____
_____
_____
_____
_____
_____
_____
_____
_____
_____
_____
_____
_____
_____
_____
_____
_____
_____
_____

Who are you currently
rescuing?

_____

_____

_____

_____

_____

_____

_____

_____

_____

_____

_____

_____

_____

_____

_____

_____

_____

_____

_____

_____

_____

_____

_____

_____

_____

_____

Tell how you need to be
rescued.

_____

_____

_____

_____

_____

_____

_____

_____

_____

_____

_____

_____

_____

_____

_____

_____

_____

_____

_____

_____

_____

_____

_____

_____

_____

_____

_____

How often do you clean (or
sage for some) your office?

_____
_____
_____
_____
_____
_____
_____
_____
_____
_____
_____
_____
_____
_____
_____
_____
_____
_____
_____
_____
_____
_____
_____
_____
_____
_____
_____

Is your space cluttered?

_____
_____
_____
_____
_____
_____
_____
_____
_____
_____
_____
_____
_____
_____
_____
_____
_____
_____
_____
_____
_____
_____
_____
_____
_____
_____
_____
_____

What's the intersection
between a messy space and
cluttered mind?

_____
_____
_____
_____
_____
_____
_____
_____
_____
_____
_____
_____
_____
_____
_____
_____
_____
_____
_____
_____
_____
_____
_____
_____
_____
_____
_____

Free write.

Free write.

References

Corey, G. Theory and Practice
of Counseling and
Pyschotherapy. 9th Ed.
California: Brooks/Cole;
2013.

Goldstein, E.D. Ego
Psychology and Social Work
Practice. 2nd Ed. New York:
The Free Press; 1995.

Kirst0-Ashman, K.K., Zastrow,
C.H. Understanding Human
Behavior and the Social
Environment. 10th Ed.
Massachusetts: Cengage
Learning; 2016.

Made in the USA
Monee, IL
23 July 2020